Writer: Joshua Ortega
Artists: Liam Sharp (Hollow)
Federico Dallocchio (One Day)

**Colors: Jonny Rench
(with Carrie Strachan #3-4)**

Letters: Wes Abbott

Covers and pinups by Brandon Badeaux,
Liam Sharp, Federico Dallocchio, Philip Tan,
Chris Perna, Stephen Platt, Shane Pierce,
and Brian Ching

Ben Abernathy	Editor-Original Series
Kristy Quinn	Assistant Editor-Original Series
Kristy Quinn	Editor
Ed Roeder	Art Director
Diane Nelson	President
Dan DiDio and Jim Lee	Co-Publishers
Geoff Johns	Chief Creative Officer
John Rood	Executive Vice President-Sales, Marketing and Busines Development
Patrick Caldon	Executive Vice President-Finance and Administration
Amy Genkins	Senior VP-Business and Legal Affairs
Steve Rotterdam	Senior VP-Sales and Marketing
John Cunningham	VP-Marketing
Terri Cunningham	VP-Managing Editor
Alison Gill	VP-Manufacturing
David Hyde	VP-Publicity
Hank Kanalz	VP-General Manager, WildStorm
Sue Pohja	VP-Book Trade Sales
Alysse Soll	VP-Advertising and Custom Publishing
Bob Wayne	VP-Sales
Mark Chiarello	Art Director

SUSTAINABLE FORESTRY INITIATIVE
Certified Chain of Custody
Promoting Sustainable
Forest Management
www.sfiprogram.org

Fiber used in this product
line meets the sourcing
requirements of the
SFI program.

www.sfiprogram.org
NSF-SFICOC-C0001801.

DC Comics, a Warner Bros. Entertainment Company.

ISBN: 978-1-4012-2541-4

Greetings!

I write this introduction returning from San Diego as I come off of the tremendous high that was the convention of Comic-Con International 2009—something that started so small years ago that is now a cultural happening, a megaton event of pop culture that celebrates this amazing medium and entertainment in general. And here we are, putting together the first hardcover edition of the GEARS OF WAR comic.

The comic book, or graphic novel, is a beloved storytelling art form that's entirely unique. I love nothing more than camping out on a beach with a good, thick trade paperback or hardbound edition and diving into a world built around framed action and boisterous sounds and bold imagery. Visiting the local comic shop and leafing through old issues or even new and exciting tales while geek-speak can be overheard in the background is a lovely way to spend an afternoon.

When we sculpted the Gears' universe we never really had time to delve into the hows and whys of each character and his or her motivation. The characters simply knew that they had to kill or be killed. Cutscenes were quick and to the point; we believe that players should be playing a game, not watching it. When the opportunity came up to partner with WildStorm we took it immediately. This was a wonderful chance to further explore the brave men and women who stood defiantly on the brink of humanity's last stand and pushed back, to find out what made them tick, and to explore what made them who they are today.

To see these characters depicted in this medium strikes a personal chord of excitement. I had to stifle a giddy little nerd laugh the first time witnessing Marcus lovingly drawn by Liam Sharp and when reading about other areas of the fiction exposed by the ever curious Joshua Ortega. The world of Sera and the war of the Gears were always built to be large, intricate and sprawling, and within these pages you're going to find more adventure, answers, and information about them than ever before.

Enjoy,

Cliff Bleszinski
Design Director, Epic Games

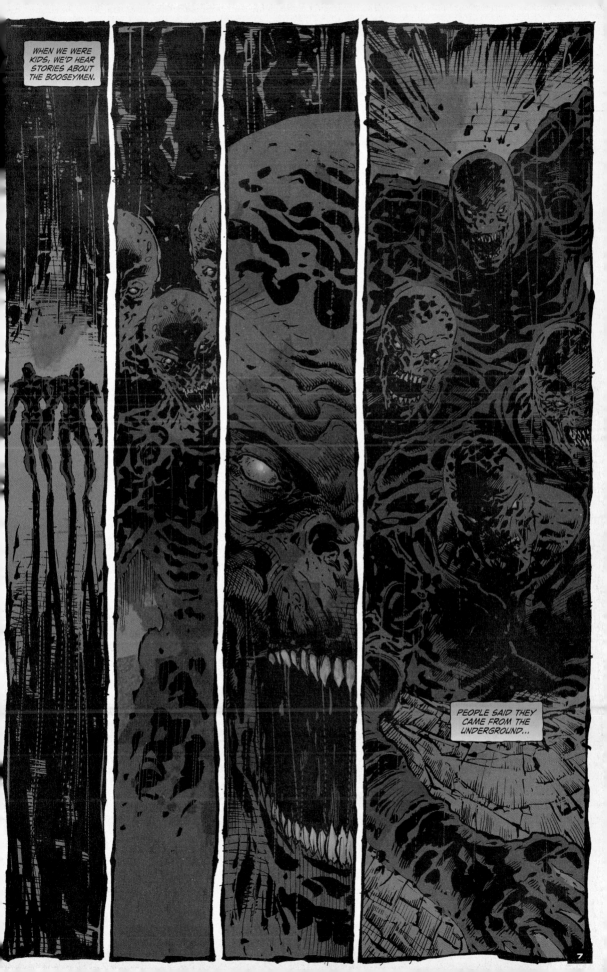

WHEN WE WERE KIDS, WE'D HEAR STORIES ABOUT THE BOOGEYMEN.

PEOPLE SAID THEY CAME FROM THE UNDERGROUND...

THE PIRNAH BADLANDS, SOUTHEAST OF JACINTO.

Fourteen years since Emergence Day. Two months after the Lightmass Bombing at Timgad.

C'MON...

GROUNDWALKER...

SHIT!

ARRAGH!

11

WHILE I WAS NEARLY GETTING MY HEAD BLOWN OFF...

...DOING MY BEST JUST TO STAY ALIVE...

...MARCUS WAS HANDLING SHIT LIKE NOBODY'S BUSINESS.

YOU'RE... URNH...YOU'RE GOIN' DOWN, GRUB...

COURSE, WE'D ALL HEARD THE STORIES ABOUT HIM...

THE PENDULUM WARS. ASPHO FIELDS. TIMGAD.

A LIVING LEGEND, RIGHT THERE IN THE FLESH.

BUT I TELL YOU, SERIOUSLY...

...THE STORIES DIDN'T DO HIM JUSTICE.

WE'D BEEN IN THE BADLANDS FOR OVER A WEEK NOW, SEARCHING FOR A FEW OF THE SQUADS THAT CONTROL HAD LOST CONTACT WITH.

YO, DOM--YOU IN THERE?

SO FAR, WE HADN'T HAD ANY LUCK...

...ALL THE SQUADS HAD BEEN KILLED OR WERE M.I.A.

APPARENTLY OUR LUCK HAD JUST CHANGED.

I THINK IT'S SAFE TO SAY HE'S IN THERE.

GUESS WHAT ME AND GIL FOUND TODAY?

ANOTHER GEAR... FINALLY.

CORPORAL MICHAEL BARRICK, ECHO SIX.

SERGEANT MARCUS FENIX, DELTA ONE. WHERE'S THE REST OF YOUR SQUAD?

YOU'RE LOOKIN' AT IT. REST OF THE SQUAD'S K.I.A.

YOU SURE THERE WEREN'T ANY SURVIVORS?

SURE AS SHIT.

SIR.

DAMN.

YOU GUYS WERE THE LAST SQUAD WE WERE SEARCHING FOR...GUESS YOU'RE HEADING BACK TO JACINTO WITH US.

DOM, I'M GONNA START UP THE APC. GATHER ANY AMMO AND COG TAGS IN THE AREA, BE READY TO HEAD OUT IN FIVE.

YOU GOT IT, MARCUS.

IT'S BARRICK, RIGHT? I'M DOM. THAT'S GIL, AND THE KID'S JACE.

SORRY TO HEAR ABOUT YOUR SQUAD, MAN.

NOT AS SORRY AS I AM.

SO YOU'RE THE NEW GEAR?

YEAH. WELL, ME AND GIL BOTH. WE WERE IN BASIC TOGETHER.

BUT YOU'RE THE KID.

SO THEY SAY.

SHITTY TIME TO BE A KID.

PENDULUM WARS WERE A BITCH, BUT THEY WERE NOTHIN' LIKE THIS LOCUST WAR. ≷COUGH≷ NO TIME FOR LIVIN' NOW.

GUESS IT'S WHAT IT IS. WE DEAL WITH IT OR DIE, RIGHT?

HEH. I LIKE THE ATTITUDE, KID.

YOU'RE A SURVIVOR. THAT'S GOOD.

LET'S ROLL.

IT WAS TOUGH NOT TO FEEL DISAPPOINTED.

THREE WEEKS OUT IN THE FIELD, AND WE'D ONLY FOUND ONE GEAR. ONE SURVIVOR.

THE APC WAS PACKED WITH AMMO AND SUPPLIES NOW, BUT STILL...

...WE NEEDED PEOPLE A LOT MORE THAN WE NEEDED SUPPLIES.

"...BUT IT'S GONNA BE A LONG RIDE."

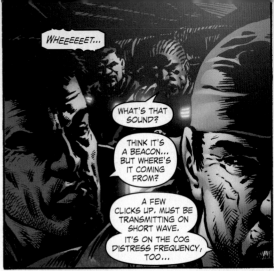

WHEEEEEET...

WHAT'S THAT SOUND?

THINK IT'S A BEACON... BUT WHERE'S IT COMING FROM?

A FEW CLICKS UP. MUST BE TRANSMITTING ON SHORT WAVE.

IT'S ON THE COG DISTRESS FREQUENCY, TOO...

"...WE SHOULD CHECK IT OUT."

THIS IS DELTA ONE! ANYBODY AROUND HERE?

NOTHING.

SO WHERE'S THE BEACON?

IT'S GOTTA BE AROUND HERE SOMEWHERE...

I THINK I FOUND SOMETHING!

WHAT DO YOU GOT?

LOOKS LIKE A TRANSMITTER TO ME.

IT IS...

...BUT THIS THING'S AT FULL POWER. AND I HAVEN'T SEEN ONE OF THESE IN ABOUT FIFTEEN YEARS...

AW, SHIT.

UNH!

ARAGH!

GIL, I NEED YOU TO HOLD THIS, MAN--APPLY PRESSURE!

ALL....ALL RIGHT...

DRONES ON THE RIGHT FLANK!

I SEE 'EM, JACE!

TWO DOWN.

NICE ONE! DOM, COVER ME!

WE GOTTA TAKE OUT THAT GODDAMN SNIPER!

THEY GOT THE DROP ON US... NO DOUBT ABOUT THAT.

ON IT!

BUT WE WERE HOLDING OUR OWN.

MORE THAN HOLDING OUR OWN.

I THOUGHT OF DOM, HIS STORY ABOUT THE IMULSION MINES...

HANG IN THERE, GEAR! C'MON!

...HOW SHIT WAS COMING FROM EVERYWHERE. PURE INSANITY.

AND FOR A SECOND, I THOUGHT WE HAD IT...I THOUGHT WE HAD THAT PLACE LOCKED DOWN.

THEN I HEARD IT...

BOOM!!

...AND I REMEMBERED THE REST OF HIS STORY.

THIS WAS ONE OF THOSE DAYS FROM HELL.

AND OF COURSE...

...THAT MEANT WE HAD BOOMERS WAITING FOR US AT THE END.

BOOM.

THEIR COVER'S BLOWN, SHIT!

THEN IT'S TIME FOR A DISTRACTION.

MARCUS!

MOVE IT, KID, MOVE IT! GET GONZALEZ OUT OF HERE!

C'MON, GIL, HANG ON, MAN...

UNH...

GIL! C'MON, MAN! WAKE UP!

FINISH 'EM OFF!

MY PLEASURE.

GIL...?

IT WASN'T THE FIRST TIME SOMEBODY DIED IN MY ARMS.

BUT THAT DIDN'T MEAN IT WAS ANY EASIER.

I REMEMBER CRYING MY EYES OUT WHEN MY BROTHER DIED...

...EVEN WITH ALL OF THE CRAZINESS ALL AROUND; I WEPT. I MOURNED.

PART OF ME WISHED I COULD STILL DO THAT...CRY, OR SCREAM, OR... SOMETHING.

BUT I JUST FELT HOLLOW. NUMB.

GIL WAS LIKE A BROTHER TO ME... AND STILL I DIDN'T HAVE ANY TEARS FOR HIM.

NOT ONE SINGLE TEAR.

JACE...

...WE GOTTA GET GOING.

JUST SEEMED WRONG SOMEHOW.

THE RIDE BACK TO JACINTO WAS A QUIET ONE.

REALLY WASN'T MUCH TO SAY.

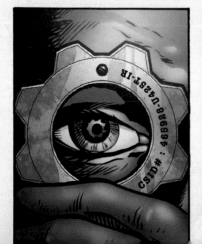

BEFORE WE EVEN WASHED OR ATE, WE TOOK CARE OF GIL...

...MADE SURE HE GOT A PROPER FUNERAL.

HE DESERVED THAT MUCH, AT LEAST.

BEFORE E-DAY, WE USED TO BURY THE DEAD...

...BUT THERE WASN'T MUCH SPACE LEFT IN JACINTO FOR PLOTS OR CEMETERIES.

AND EVEN MORESO...

THERE WAS NO DAMN WAY WE WERE EVER GONNA PUT OUR PEOPLE INTO THE GROUND AGAIN.

BENEATH US WAS HELL.

HEAVEN'S ABOVE...

...AND THAT'S WHERE WE ALL DESERVE TO BE.

GONE, YES.

COMPLETELY GONE, AS FAR AS WE CAN TELL.

UNFORTUNATELY, IT'S ALSO CLEAR NOW THAT MANY LOCUST SURVIVED THE ATTACK--HOW MANY, WE DO NOT KNOW--BUT AT LEAST HUMANITY CAN FEEL A LITTLE BIT SAFER AT NIGHT.

THAT WAS THE WORD FROM CHAIRMAN PRESCOTT TODAY AS HE ADDRESSED THE SOVEREIGN PRESS CORPS ABOUT THE RECENT DISAPPEARANCE OF KRYLL AFTER THE LIGHTMASS BOMBING AT TIMGAD.

IN OTHER NEWS, TREMORS CONTINUE TO BE FELT IN AREAS AROUND JACINTO...

JAYSON? JAYSON STRATTON?

YEAH?

MR. WISEMAN SAID TO SEND YOU ON BACK.

COOL, THANKS.

HOW WAS THE WEEK, JACE?

JUST READY TO GET BACK OUT THERE, MAN. I DON'T LIKE HAVING TOO MUCH TIME TO THINK.

YEAH, I HEAR YOU...

NOT BAD. SAW A FEW FRIENDS, DROPPED BY SOME OLD HAUNTS...

NOTHING SPECIAL, REALLY. YOU?

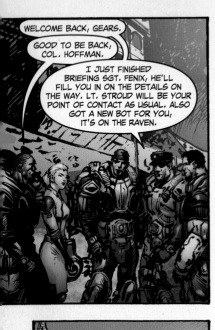

WELCOME BACK, GEARS.

GOOD TO BE BACK, COL. HOFFMAN.

I JUST FINISHED BRIEFING SGT. FENIX, HE'LL FILL YOU IN ON THE DETAILS ON THE WAY. LT. STROUD WILL BE YOUR POINT OF CONTACT AS USUAL. ALSO GOT A NEW BOT FOR YOU, IT'S ON THE RAVEN.

YOU'RE ALL READY TO GO. GOOD LUCK OUT THERE.

LET'S GET MOVING, DELTA.

DOM...

YEAH?

I'M STILL LOOKING FOR HER, OKAY? JUST SO YOU KNOW.

...THANKS.

I'LL SEE YOU SOON, ANYA.

WAIT A SEC-- SHOULDN'T WE BE ROLLING A FOUR-MAN SQUAD?

WE ARE.

DORADO HILLS. BETWEEN JACINTO AND MONTEVADO.

SEISMICS?

SHIT, ≥COUGH≤ WE'VE BEEN HAVING THOSE SINCE E-DAY.

THESE ARE DIFFERENT. A WHOLE LOT BIGGER.

WHAT, LIKE EARTHQUAKES?

IF WE'RE LUCKY.

ANY OTHER SQUADS GONNA BE OUT THERE?

SIGMA ONE MIGHT BE IN THE NEXT VALLEY OVER. WE'LL SEE.

HOPE SO. IT'D BE GOOD TO SEE COLE AGAIN... BAIRD...NOT SO MUCH.

BEING UP THERE, IN THE SKY...

...IT MADE ME THINK OF GIL'S FUNERAL AGAIN.

HOW LONG BEFORE WE ≤COUGH≥ HIT MONTEVADO?

STILL A WAYS.

YOU KNOW THAT SHIT'S GONNA KILL YOU, RIGHT?

HELL, *WAR* WILL KILL YOU. SMOKING'S THE LEAST OF MY WORRIES.

HOW LIFE GOES BY SO FAST...

SERGEANT FENIX?

YEAH?

I'M GETTING SOME UNUSUAL READINGS ON RAD--

BOOM

...HOW LIFE CAN TURN TO DEATH IN AN INSTANT.

IT ALSO MADE ME THINK OF HEAVEN...

AH!

JACE!

I HESITATED AT FIRST...

CAN ANYONE FLY ONE OF THESE THINGS?!

NO! I DON'T EVEN LIKE FLYING!

THAT DOESN'T HELP US!

...HOPING THERE'D BE ANOTHER WAY.

WE GOT ANY PARACHUTES IN HERE?!

WE DID UNTIL THEY CAUGHT FIRE!

MARCUS...

THEN I REALIZED IT WAS ALL ME.

...I MIGHT BE ABLE TO GET US DOWN.

THEN GET YOUR ASS UP HERE!

NOT GOOD.

YOU EVER FLOWN ONE OF THESE BEFORE?

ONCE...

...BUT I DIDN'T HAVE TO LAND IT.

SHIT.

PULL UP, MAN--C'MON, YOU'RE GETTING TOO CLOSE!

BOOM

GREAT, THERE GOES THE LANDING GEAR!

MAN UP, BARRICK! AND GET OUT OF HIS EAR, LET HIM DO HIS JOB!

THAT WAS THE MOMENT.

THAT WAS WHEN I KNEW I COULD DO IT.

EVERYONE BRACE YOURSELVES-- I'M ABOUT TO LAND THIS THING!

IF MARCUS FENIX HAD FAITH IN ME...

BUT WE GOT AN E-HOLE UP THERE! THEY'RE GONNA BE ALL OVER US!

...THEN I'D DAMN WELL BETTER HAVE FAITH IN MYSELF.

THE HELL THEY WILL.

DID STAN MAKE IT?

STAN?

OUR BOT-- STAN.

GUESS THAT ANSWERS THE QUESTION...STILL CAN CLOAK, TOO.

ALL RIGHT, I'M NOT COMPLAINING WE SURVIVED, BUT...WHERE THE HELL IS MONTEVADO FROM HERE?

NOT SURE.

CONTROL, THIS IS DELTA, DO YOU READ ME?

JUST STATIC.

SEEDERS MUST BE TOO CLOSE STILL, JAMMING EVERYTHING.

SO WHICH WAY'S MONTEVADO?

I THINK IT'S OVER THOSE HILLS...

...BUT WE GOT A WAYS TO GO.

THEN LET'S GET TO IT.

BARRICK WASN'T KIDDING.

WE WALKED FOR DAYS...

LOOK AT THE BRIGHT SIDE...

...AT LEAST WE DON'T HAVE TO WALK ALL THIS WAY IN ARMOR.

HA...REMIND ME TO LAUGH WHEN WE'RE DONE WITH THIS SHIT.

...WITHOUT A SIGN OF ANYTHING...

...OR ANYBODY.

SOMEBODY UP AHEAD.

HOSTILE?

DON'T THINK SO.

YOU'RE SPOTTED-- GET OUT OF THERE. HANDS WHERE I CAN SEE 'EM.

FAIR ENOUGH... I AIN'T STUPID ENOUGH TO FIGHT A SQUAD OF GEARS.

WHAT ARE YOU DOING OUT HERE?

WAS JUST ABOUT TO ASK YOU THE SAME THING...

WE'RE EN ROUTE TO MONTEVADO...YOU KNOW THE BEST WAY FROM HERE?

MONTEVADO? SHIT, YOU'RE A WAYS OUT, BROTHER. YOU NEED A VEHICLE TO REACH THAT PLACE...

THAT MEAN YOU GOT A RIG?

MAYBE.

WE DON'T HAVE TIME FOR MAYBE. YES OR NO?

YEAH, I HEAR YOU. FOLLOW ME... I'LL SEE WHAT I CAN DO. AND BY THE WAY, NAME'S JONBOY...

FUCKED

HERE WE ARE...

WELCOME TO FUCKED.

BEYOND JACINTO, HUMANITY LIVED A WHOLE DIFFERENT EXISTENCE.

WHAT?

FUCKED. THAT'S WHAT THIS PLACE IS, THAT'S WHAT WE CALL IT.

WHEN THE LOCUST ATTACKED ON E-DAY, THE COG TOLD EVERYONE TO RETREAT TO JACINTO.

THOSE WHO ARRIVED IN TIME... THEY MADE THEIR HOMES WITHIN WALLS OF RELATIVE SAFETY.

THOSE WHO DIDN'T...

HOW LONG YOU BEEN OUT HERE?

PRETTY MUCH SINCE E-DAY... BUT THINGS GOT WORSE RECENTLY. SOMETHING STIRRED UP THE LOCUST AGAIN.

...THEY HAD TO FEND FOR THEMSELVES.

THE STRANDED. THAT'S WHAT WE CALL THEM.

"FUCKED" SEEMS EVEN MORE APPROPRIATE.

PROBABLY THE LIGHTMASS BOMB...

SO WHAT'S THE SITUATION? WE NEED TO GET TO MONTEVADO...CAN YOU HELP?

HOPE SO...

...BUT I GOTTA ASK--WHAT CAN YOU DO FOR US?

PROBABLY THE FIRST TIME I EVER FELT LIKE A HERO.

WE ABSOLUTELY MOPPED THOSE BASTARDS.

SO JONBOY-- WHERE'S THAT VEHICLE?

HOPE FOR YOUR SAKE YOU WEREN'T BULLSHITTING US.

HAHA, SHIT, BROTHER, DON'T YOU WORRY...

...WE GOT YOU COVERED.

IT WAS A TRIP BEING OUT THERE...BEING AROUND THESE PEOPLE WHO HAD SURVIVED SO LONG, WITHOUT ANY HELP FROM THE COG.

COULDN'T HELP BUT FEEL PROUD OF THE HUMAN SPIRIT...AND ADMITTEDLY, I EVEN FELT A BIT OF HOPE.

HOPE FOR HUMANITY.

ESPECIALLY THE KID...

VE!

YOU GOT A *KID* HERE?

YEAH...HER PARENTS ROLLED OUT TO MONTEVADO, TRIED TO GET SOME HELP. THOUGHT IT WAS TOO DANGEROUS TO TAKE HER...

WHAT, THEY THOUGHT HERE WAS SAFE?

BROTHER... AIN'T NOWHERE SAFE.

YOU BEEN WAITING FOR YOUR PARENTS?

...

...YEAH.

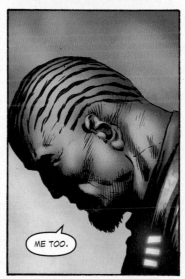

ME TOO.

ALL RIGHT, DELTA, GATHER UP YOUR SHIT AND LET'S GET INTO THE JUNKER. WE GOTTA GET TO MONTEVADO.

YOU WANT TO GO WITH US?

I DON'T KNOW...

...MAYBE?

MARCUS--

--CAN WE TAKE THE TAKE THE KID WITH US?

WHAT?

JACE, I UNDERSTAND WHAT YOU'RE FEELIN', BUT...

REMEMBER, SOLDIER...WE CALL THIS PLACE *FUCKED* FOR A REASON.

...

ALL RIGHT...

"...THE KID ROLLS WITH US."

SO WHAT'S YOUR NAME?

LILY.

SHE TOLD ME HER NAME RIGHT OFF THE BAT. SWEET LITTLE KID, JUST WANTING TO BE BACK WITH HER FOLKS.

FELT LIKE I HAD TO GIVE HER HOPE...

YOU KNOW WE'RE GONNA FIND YOUR PARENTS, RIGHT?

I PROMISE YOU--WE'LL FIND 'EM.

...EVEN IF I KNEW IT WAS GONNA BE A LONGSHOT.

WHEN I CAME OUT OF THAT RIDE, I FELT LIKE NOTHING COULD STOP ME...

...A KID'S LIFE DEPENDED ON ME.

WASN'T ANYTHING THAT WAS GONNA STOP ME.

REALITY SUCKS SOMETIMES.

ROOOAR

BRUMAK!

AW NO, NOT NOW...

CONTROL, THIS IS DELTA-- WE'VE GOT A BRUMAK! NEED BACKUP, ASAP!!

CONTROL, REPEAT, THIS IS DELTA--WE NEED SOME FUCKING BACKUP!!

SEEDERS ARE STILL JAMMING EVERYTHING! USE THE SHORTWAVE, THAT'S OUR ON--

OH FUCK...

HOLLOW
PART FOUR

GET YOUR ASS UP, JACE-- C'MON!

DOM AND BARRICK FOUND COVER, MOVE!

HOW THE HELL ARE WE SUPPOSED TO KILL A BRUMAK WITH THIS KIND OF FIREPOWER?!

HONESTLY?

WE CAN'T.

THIS IS DELTA ONE, ANYBODY IN THE MONTEVADO AREA, WE *NEED* BACKUP ASAP!!

BOOM, BABY--YOU FEELIN' THAT SHIT?!

COLE...?

COLE, GET YOUR ASS BACK IN HERE! DISTRACTION ACHIEVED, BUT WE GOTTA GO!

THEN LAY SOME TRACKS, BAIRD!

FWOOM

NICE ONE, BABY!

WE'LL SEE--IF WE'RE NOT BLEEDING OUT IN 20 MINUTES I'LL TAKE THE COMPLIMENT!

GET US THE HELL OUT OF HERE! THE REST OF THE SQUAD IS UP AHEAD!

YOU'RE WELCOME.

EVERYONE, GET IN!

FIRST THING I DID WAS CHECK ON LILY.

IF SOMETHING HAPPENED TO HER...

...IF I'D BETRAYED THAT LITTLE GIRL'S TRUST...

...I'D FEEL LIKE A PART OF ME DIED AGAIN.

IN THIS CASE...

FATE DEALT US A DECENT HAND.

JACE...

...I WAS SCARED.

IT'S OKAY...

"...I WAS TOO."

YO, MAN, THERE WAS A LITTLE GIRL IN THAT RIDE?

DAMN, MARCUS, YOU PLAY THAT SHIT TOO CLOSE SOMETIMES.

YOU DO WHAT YOU GOTTA DO.

SO HOW THE HELL DID YOU FIND US, COLE?

TURNS OUT COLE AND BAIRD HAD BEEN PART OF DELTA BEFORE ME AND BARRICK...

THEY'D BEEN WITH MARCUS AND DOM AT TIMGAD, AT THE LIGHTMASS BOMBING, AND WERE NOW LEADING THEIR OWN SQUAD, SIGMA ONE.

GOTCHA.

WELL, SOUNDS LIKE YOU GUYS ARE ROLLING BACK WITH US NOW--'CAUSE I DON'T HAVE THE PARTS TO FIX THIS PIECE OF SHIT.

WHO SAYS WE NEED THAT SHIT?

THESE HAVE ENOUGH JUICE IN 'EM TO GET US TO MONTEVADO?

YEAH, THINK SO. BUT, C'MON, MAN, YOU CAN'T TAKE A KID ON THOSE THINGS, THAT'S LIKE CHILD ABUSE OR SOMETHING...

OH WAIT-- PLEASE. NO. C'MON... BABYSITTING? REALLY?

YOU'RE HEADING TO JACINTO. YOU JUST GOT AN EXTRA PASSENGER.

JACE, THE KID'S GOING BACK WITH SIGMA TO JACINTO. IT'LL BE A LOT SAFER THERE THAN OUT HERE.

YOU'RE GONNA GO BACK TO JACINTO WITH COLE AND BAIRD, OKAY, LILY? IT'S A SAFE PLACE. I'LL CHECK ON YOU WHEN WE GET BACK-- I PROMISE.

OKAY... I GUESS. JACE-- ARE YOU GONNA FIND MY PARENTS?

...

I'M GONNA DO MY BEST.

WE SET OUT FOR MONTEVADO ON THE BIKES, JUST ENOUGH FUEL TO GET US TO THE CITY.

MARCUS TOLD SIGMA TO SEND A RAVEN TO MONTEVADO TOMORROW.

GOTTA GIVE HIM CREDIT FOR BEING HOPEFUL.

TALK ABOUT A GHOST TOWN...

FOR REAL.

≡COUGH≡ SO WHAT'S A SEISMIC DISTURBANCE SUPPOSED TO LOOK LIKE?

YOU SERIOUS?

RIGHT.

SERIOUSLY THOUGH, WE JUST SUPPOSED TO HANG OUT ≡COUGH≡ AND SEE IF THE GROUND SHAKES?

HE'S GOT A POINT. IT'S NOT LIKE THEY GAVE US ANY EQUIPMENT OR MEASURING DEVICES...

TYPICAL MILITARY MISSION... WE JUST GOTTA WORK WITH WHAT WE HAVE.

DOM, JACE, YOU GUYS CHECK OUT THE NORTHERN PART OF TOWN. BARRICK AND I WILL TAKE THE SOUTH.

STAY IN CONTACT AT ALL TIMES, AND TRY TO KEEP A LOW PROFILE...